*

Never Hide a Hyena in a Sack

and other folk stories from Africa

by Ines Penny

Cover and illustrations
by Doug Driediger

An SIM publication

Never Hide a Hyena in a Sack

© 1984 by SIM International

ISBN: 0-919470-09-2

Library of Congress Catalog Card No. 84-50223

Printed in Canada

First Printing, 1984
Second Printing, 1986

SIM Offices

Australia: P.O. Box 371, Miranda, N.S.W. 2228

Canada: 10 Huntingdale Blvd., Scarborough, Ontario M1W 2S5

Great Britain: Ullswater Crescent, Coulsdon
Surrey, CR3 2HR, England

New Zealand: P.O. Box 38588, Howick

Singapore: Bras Basah, P.O. Box 239, Singapore 9118

Southern Africa: Private Bag 5, Westhoven
Johannesburg 2142, S. Africa

Switzerland: Rue de Genève 77 bis, CH-1004 Lausanne

U.S.A.: Box 7900, Charlotte, NC 28217

Contents

Never Hide a Hyena in a Sack

Once there was a farmer named Walday. He was a good farmer, but he often got himself into trouble trying to please everyone. One day Walday was working on his farm. Suddenly he heard shouts in the distance, and a hyena dashed out of the bushes. "Save me!" Hyena gasped. "The hunters are after me and I can't run any more!"

"Well," Walday replied, "I would like to help you, but I really don't know how."

"Hide me!" Hyena panted. "Hide me in that sack!"

"Very well," Walday replied, and helped Hyena into the sack, which was made of strong leather. Then he tied the top and sat it up as though it had grain in it.

The hunters arrived carrying clubs and spears. "Have you seen that dreadful hyena?" they asked. "We saw him running this way."

Walday avoided the question. "Would I be standing here if I had seen him?" he answered.

"Watch out for him!" the hunters warned. "Don't let him make a meal of you!"

After they had gone, Walday let Hyena out of the sack. Then he went back to work. But Hyena didn't leave. He just sat watching Walday...with a hungry look in his eye.

"Isn't it time you were on your way?" asked Walday nervously. "The hunters may return."

"I must eat first, or I will not be able to run," answered Hyena, licking his lips.

"Now just a minute," said Walday. "You wouldn't think of eating the one who saved your life, would you?"

"Why not?" answered Hyena. "Surely you didn't save my life just so I could starve to death?"

"But that would not be fair!" Walday protested.

"Who says so?" retorted Hyena. "Is there a law against it?"

Walday was frightened. "We must find a judge," he said. "A judge must decide."

Walday hoped the hunters would think it was just a sack of grain.

That was the custom of the forest, so Hyena had to agree.

The first animal they went to was Rabbit. He listened to the story, then said: "In my judgment, anyone who is foolish enough to save the life of a hyena deserves to be eaten," and he hopped away.

"He just said that because he is afraid of you," cried Walday. "I insist on finding another judge!"

"Very well," said Hyena. "We'll try Lion. He's not afraid of me."

So Lion heard the story, but he, too, agreed with Rabbit. "To save the life of a hyena is a foolish thing to do," he said. "As far as I'm concerned, you can eat him."

"Please!" Walday begged Hyena. "Please! Let us find one more judge...a *really* wise one."

"You must mean Monkey," Hyena replied. "He's the smartest of them all."

So they told the story to Monkey. When they had finished, Monkey looked at them sternly and said: "I do not believe either one of you. A hyena cannot hide in a sack."

"But I did!" Hyena protested. "Walday helped me get in."

"I'll believe that when I see it," Monkey replied. "Show me!"

So Walday helped Hyena get back into the sack.

"And how was the sack tied?" Monkey demanded.

"Like this," said Walday, and showed him.

"Now," said Monkey to Walday, with a wink, "I understand that you farmers thresh your grain by putting it in a sack and beating it with a stick. May I have a demonstration, please?"

Monkey was not only clever, he was wise. He helped Walday learn from his mistake. If we are wise, we will learn from our mistakes, too. The best way to do that is to read God's Word, so we will know how we should behave. A king named Solomon became one of the wisest judges who ever lived because he asked God to help him. He prayed: "Now give me wisdom and knowledge" (2 Chronicles 1:10). You can pray that prayer, too.

The Goat Well

Long ago a man named Atalie, which means deceiver, was traveling through a lonely place in the mountains of Ethiopia. He sat down by the path to eat his noon meal. Suddenly the quietness was broken by the bleating of a goat. He looked all around, but didn't see anything. After a while he heard the bleating again. But still he could see no goat. He began to search and soon found an old well that had dried up.

Cautiously, he looked in. There at the bottom he saw a goat.

"Luck is with me!" said Atalie, delighted. "I will pull this goat out and sell it!"

He took off the cloth that he wore over his shoulders and tore it into strips. Then he tied them together to make a rope, lowered himself into the well, and tied the rope around the goat. He climbed back out, and started to pull. Just then a trader came along leading three heavily loaded camels.

"I come in peace," said Trader. "I would like water for myself and my camels."

Atalie thought quickly. "I would gladly give you water," he replied, "but this is not a water well. It's a goat well."

"A goat well!" exclaimed Trader. "I have never heard of such a thing. Why do you say it is a goat well?"

"Because every day I get a fine goat like this out of it," lied Atalie, pulling the goat the rest of the way out of the well.

Trader thought: "A goat every day! I'd soon be rich!" He

Trader could hardly wait until it was time to look into the well.

wanted that well.

Out loud he said: "You know, I'm tired of traveling. I'll give you these camels, and their loads too, if you will give me your goat well."

Atalie sighed. "I have so many goats that they are now a burden to me," he said. "Yes, I will give you the goat well. This is what you must do. Take this goat, cut off its horns, and throw them into the well at sunset. Tomorrow when the sun is high overhead you will hear the bleating of a goat. Then, and only then, you may look into the well...and draw up your goat."

Trader took the goat, and Atalie rode off with the camels and grain.

After he had gone, Trader cut off the goat's horns and waited impatiently for the sun to set. Then he threw the horns into the well and lay down to sleep.

He awoke very early the next morning. Was it time to pull his goat out of the well? No, the sun was still low. Very slowly it crept across the sky until at last it was directly overhead.

Trader sat close to the well and waited to hear the first bleat of his goat. But there was only silence. Trader waited a long time. He didn't want to spoil the magic.

In fact, he waited until the sun began to go down and his shadow grew long. When he finally got up enough courage to look into the well, all he saw was two dirty horns.

Sick at heart, Trader turned slowly from the well.

"I have been deceived," he wailed. "I have no goats, no camels, no goods...nothing!"

There is somebody out to deceive *you,* just as Atalie tricked Trader. The Bible calls him Satan. He whispers: "Do as I tell you and you'll have lots of good things." Don't believe him. Listen to Jesus instead; you won't be disappointed. His message to us is: "For God so loved the world that He gave His only begotten Son, that whoever believes in Him should not perish but have everlasting life" (John 3:16).

Dog and Chameleon

Strange as it may seem, Dog and Chameleon were very good friends. Every day they went to the stream for a drink. Chameleon would start out first, but Dog would always race past her, and arrive at the stream long before she did. When Chameleon finally arrived, Dog would tease her for being so slow. Sometimes Chameleon would scold him good-naturedly. "Listen, you foolish dog," she would say. "Don't always do things in such a rush. Learn to move carefully. I fear what may happen if you don't."

But Dog would only laugh. "You do what you want, and I'll do what I want," he would answer. "Each to his own. If the neighbor of a man who keeps goats buys a hyena for his pet, that's his business."

So the days passed, Dog always on the run, and Chameleon plodding steadily along.

All was well until one day some women pounded grain into flour, and spread it out to dry on a big, flat rock. Dog came along, traveling at his usual speed, and couldn't stop in time. He went right through the flour, scattering it everywhere. The angry women caught him and gave him a beating.

Chameleon was very sad at what had happened to her friend, and went to visit him.

She sat beside Dog, who was too sore and bruised to move, and tried her best to comfort him. "I'm so sorry, Dog," she said tearfully. "What I warned you about has happened. The one who does not hear 'stop' will be sorry one day. If we do not tread this old world carefully we'll end up in trouble."

"What I warned you about has happened," Chameleon told Dog tearfully.

Many people, like Dog, don't listen to warnings. But when trouble comes, they wish they had. The Bible gives us a very important warning: "How shall we escape if we neglect so great a salvation?" (Hebrews 2:3). If we refuse God's offer of salvation we cannot go to heaven.

Have you done something about that warning? Have you received the Lord Jesus into your heart as your Savior? If so, are you passing God's warning on to others?

Miserable Advice

The storm was over. Sarki, the chief of foxes, stepped out of his den. "Wind blows down palm nuts," he said. "And where there are palm nuts there are rats. Today I will feast on rats!"

Sarki stretched himself and proudly waved his bushy tail back and forth. "The finest tail in the world," he bragged. It was truly a fine tail.

He hurried toward a nearby palm tree. Beside it was a big thorn bush. Sarki stretched out on his stomach under the palm tree with his nose between his front paws and his tail stretched out behind. The breeze played with his tail, lifting it dangerously close to the thorns.

Soon rats came to gather nuts. A big rat came close to Sarki. He sprang to catch it, but couldn't. His tail was caught fast in the thorn bush. He twisted and turned, wriggled and rolled, but he could not pull himself free.

The rats filled themselves with their favorite nuts, then left him alone. Sarki struggled again and again to free himself. Finally he gave a mighty pull, and was free. But his tail wasn't...it remained swinging in the thorn bush.

Hurting and ashamed, Sarki crept home and hid in the darkest corner of his den.

"Without my tail, I can never again appear in public," he whimpered. He knew he could never be happy without his beautiful tail.

For several days he stayed in his den, miserable and alone. Then he had an idea. He ordered all the foxes to come. "I hope this works," he said to himself while he waited for

13

The foxes were angry when their tailless chief tried to trick them.

them to gather. When they were all present, Sarki crawled halfway out of his den.

"My friends," he began, trying to smile, "I have called you here to tell you about a wonderful discovery. My tail, like yours, was a nuisance because it was always getting full of tangles and burrs. Finally I found the answer. I have cut it off. Now I have great freedom and comfort, and I want all of you to do as I did. Then you, too, can enjoy life more and be happier."

Then, though burning with embarrassment, Sarki came out and stood before them all. "Look!" he said, "No tail, no burrs, no trouble!"

The thought of having no tail shocked the foxes. But would their chief advise them to do something that was not for their good?

Old Gray Fox saw that Sarki was determined to have his own way. "Friends, listen to me," he said. "Our chief says he is happy to be free from the burden of his tail. But is his a happy face? Did he really cut off his tail because he chose to? Ask him if he did not lose his tail in the thorn bush!" And he held up the missing tail.

The foxes could hardly believe what they saw. "Sarki Fox shows no joy," Old Gray Fox continued sternly. "So I say: Beware of the advice of a miserable animal."

The foxes looked again at their tailless chief. Then, one by one, they made their way home, leaving Sarki alone with his misery.

There are many people who have lost their happiness because they chose to go their own way instead of obeying God. Sometimes they tell others: "It's too difficult to serve the Lord. Don't be a missionary. Don't go to some far away place. You will be happier if you stay at home."

Remember what Old Gray Fox said: "Don't listen to the advice of a miserable animal." Listen instead to the Bible: "Blessed is the man who walks not in the counsel of the ungodly....But his delight is in the law of the Lord" (Psalm 1:1).

Farmer and Lion

One day a farmer named Wawantaka, which means foolishness, met a lion on the path. They eyed each other suspiciously. At last Lion greeted Wawantaka. "Good morning, O man with the beard of wisdom," he purred. "I am Lion, the king of the beasts. May I walk with you, O wise one?"

Wawantaka was flattered with this greeting, and agreed to walk with him. Lion continued to flatter the farmer about his good looks, his wisdom, and his courage.

Wawantaka passed many friends along the way. They all warned him to run for his life. But Wawantaka only laughed. "This is my friend," he said. "He will not harm me."

After a while, however, Lion and Wawantaka began to argue.

"Man is superior to the lion," Wawantaka insisted. "He is wiser and stronger."

"No," growled Lion. "The lion is superior to man."

The argument got very hot.

"Man is superior!" Wawantaka shouted.

"He is not!" Lion roared.

Just then they heard the angry snarl of a lion coming from around a bend in the path.

"Did you hear that?" Wawantaka said proudly. "It is the sound of a lion in trouble. He has been trapped by man. Does this not prove that man is superior?"

"It doesn't prove anything," replied Lion angrily, "except that you are just like your name...foolish. Allow me to show you the lion's superior wisdom and his superior strength...right now!"

With that Lion pounced on the farmer and pinned him to the ground. "I fooled you with my superior wisdom by flattering you," he boasted. "Now I will finish you off with my superior strength!"

Flattery is the gateway to trouble. The Bible says: "A man who flatters his neighbor spreads a net for his feet" (Proverbs 29:5). How careful we must be not to let flattery become a trap to us. It can keep us from listening to God and doing His will.

Leopard and the Monkeys

Leopard lay quietly in a shady spot thinking about chickens, and goats, and pigs. He was old, tired, and very hungry. "What I'd really like," he muttered, "is some juicy monkey meat." But Leopard knew that he could no longer run fast or climb trees. So how could he catch a monkey?

Suddenly his eyes gleamed. "I may not be as strong or as quick as I used to be," he chuckled, "but my mind is still clever. I'll catch them by tricks."

He got up slowly and moved through the tall grass, stopping below the monkeys' favorite mango tree. He knew they were watching him.

"People of the trees," he called, "I've come to visit you." Not a sound came from the tree.

"Come and be my friends," purred Leopard. "I want to live in peace with you."

Then Monkey Chief spoke. "Can a leopard truly speak words of peace?" he asked.

"When I was young I was wild and wicked," answered Leopard sadly. "But now I am old and I want to live in peace."

"What else do you want?" asked Monkey Chief sternly.

"What I really want," replied Leopard, "is to learn your ways, especially your jumping skill, and to live happily with you."

"You have many enemies because you are deceitful," scolded Monkey Chief. "My people and I must discuss this."

The monkeys got together in the highest branches, where Leopard couldn't hear them. "It's a trick," they said.

Poor Leopard was left swinging by his tail.

"Leopard thinks only of monkey meat."

"Let's test him," suggested wise old Chief. They worked out a plan, and Monkey Chief dropped to a lower branch.

"Leopard," he said sternly, lowering a small basket, "take this home with you. But do not take the lid off for any reason. If you bring it back tomorrow, unopened, we will teach you to jump like we do."

When Leopard got home he threw the basket in a corner. He and his wife laughed and talked all evening about monkey meat. "We'll grow fat as we grow old," they said. "When they teach us how to jump like they do, we can catch as many of them as we wish."

Early the next morning, Leopard tied the basket securely to the rope that was still dangling from the mango tree. Immediately the basket was lifted into the highest branches, out of sight. When Monkey Chief opened it, out jumped his smallest son. The little monkey excitedly whispered what he had heard at Leopard's home. All the monkeys were very angry.

Monkey Chief called to Leopard: "Because you have done as we told you," he said, "we will now teach you to jump like we do. But first you must learn to eat our food." And he threw down a large mango.

Greedy Leopard pounced on it and bit into it so hard that he broke a tooth. He didn't know that the fruit had a large, hard seed in the middle of it. "Oooowwww!" he howled in pain.

"So sorry," sympathized Monkey Chief. But Leopard could not see his big smile. "Maybe this will help your pain," Monkey Chief said as he threw down a hot pepper.

Leopard bit carefully this time, and was happy that there was no hard seed inside. But after a few bites his mouth and throat began to burn. He jumped up and down, yelling: "Ooww, my mouth is burning! Water! Water!" He gasped and choked while tears streamed from his eyes.

"I see you like our food," said Monkey Chief. "You are shouting for joy, and you are already beginning to jump. Now you are ready for the first lesson on how to jump like we do."

Monkey Chief and two strong monkeys dropped to a

low branch. Leopard was excited by their closeness. His mouth began to water.

"First you must hold up your tail tall and straight, like this," said the Chief, holding up his own tail. "Now, hold it up as high as you can. Higher! Good!"

Suddenly, strong monkey arms grabbed Leopard's tail and pulled him right off the ground. Quickly they tied his tail to a big sturdy branch, while a chorus of monkey laughter filled the air. Poor Leopard was left swinging by his tail...and that is why, ever since, a leopard's tail has such a big, round curve.

Leopard's problem wasn't his tail...it was his heart, which was filled with deceit. The Bible says: "The heart is deceitful above all things, and desperately wicked" (Jeremiah 17:9). Deceitful hearts are unhappy hearts. God wants us to have clean, happy ones, so He sent Jesus to die in our place on the cross. When we trust in Jesus, God forgives us. Then we can be truly happy, and share the good news with others.

The Stolen Tray

It was market day. Excitement was in the air. It was a time to buy and sell and visit and catch up on all the news. A few people, however, had different thoughts about market day...dishonest thoughts.

Two of these people, a man and his wife, lived in a house at the edge of town. He was a thief. So was she. One day he entered the kitchen where his wife was preparing bean cakes. From under the folds of his long robe he took a beautiful brass tray that he had stolen.

"I want you to sell this in the market today," he said.

"It is done," replied his wife confidently.

She hid the tray under the cloth which covered her large pan of bean cakes, and made her way to market.

After a while a man approached her. Cautiously, she took the tray from under the cloth and showed it to him. "I will buy it," he said at last. "How much?" They haggled for a while and finally agreed on a price. It was a good price. Her husband would be pleased.

The man took the tray and said he would be right back with the money. But time passed and he did not return.

She finished selling all her bean cakes, but still he did not come. She waited until the sun was low in the west. Then she realized that he, too, was a thief. The tray had disappeared for good.

Wearily, she made her way home. She found her husband had several visitors.

"Was business good today?" her husband asked, eager to know about the tray, but not wanting to mention it in front of the visitors.

"Very good," she replied.

Then he asked slyly: "For how much did you sell?"

Just as slyly she replied: "As you bought, so I sold."

There was nothing more to be said. As they had done to another, so it was done to them.

The people in this story were thieves. They were mean to other people. Perhaps that is why someone else was mean to them. Jesus taught us that we should treat others kindly and honestly. He said: "Just as you want men to do to you, you also do to them likewise" (Luke 6:31). When somebody told you about Jesus, that was a very good and kind thing to do. You can do a good thing, too, by telling somebody else. Maybe, when you're older, you can be a missionary to people in parts of the world who don't know anything about Him.

23

The Dirty Well

"We want water! We want water!" The cry of angry women rang through the town as they marched to the chief's house. When the chief appeared they all began to shout at once. "Silence!" he commanded. "Let one person tell me your problem."

An elderly woman was pushed forward. "Long may you live," she began, bowing low. "We can no longer drink the terrible well water. It is too dirty and smelly!"

"I will do my best to help you," the chief promised, and went to discuss the problem with his wise men.

"Maybe they'll use the water if they don't look at it," suggested one man. So a blind man was called to draw the water out of the well and give it to the women. But even though he could not see the water, the women could. They refused to use it.

"Perhaps a new bucket will help," another man suggested. Soon a shiny new bucket was lowered into the well. But the water it brought up was still dirty.

"It needs strong medicine," said a very old man. But when the witch doctor had used up all his medicine and magic, the water was as bad as ever.

Then a young man spoke up. "A pump is the answer!" he announced. What excitement there was when a beautiful new pump was installed! But the water which gushed out of it was still dirty and smelly.

The chief was sad. "What shall we do to get clean water?" he asked.

A stranger stepped up. "Long may you live, O Chief,"

There seemed to be no end to the dirty things in the bottom of the well.

he said, bowing low. "I know how to get good water."

"I do not know you," answered the chief. "But if you can help us solve our problem we will be grateful."

The stranger ordered several strong men to lower him by a rope into the well. Then they lowered buckets for him to fill. The people watched as the men pulled up the buckets that had sticks, rags, leaves, and dead snakes and lizards in them. Finally, they pulled the stranger out.

"Now empty the well and let it fill up with water again," he ordered. They did. Then the stranger took a bucket of water to the chief and said: "Long may you live, O Chief. Try the water now."

The chief looked into the bucket. The water was clear and clean. He took a long drink and smiled. The crowd cheered.

"The water could not be changed by medicine or a new pump," the stranger explained. "The trouble was the dirt inside the well. The only way to have clean water is to have a clean well."

"The whole town thanks you," the chief said as he shook the stranger's hand.

"Remember," the stranger replied, "only a clean well will give clean water. Take care never to let dirt gather in this well again."

Dirt in a well is like sin in a heart. A life cannot be good in God's sight when a heart is dirty with sin. Only the Lord Jesus Christ can make sinful hearts clean. The Bible says: "The blood of Jesus Christ His Son cleanses us from all sin" (1 John 1:7). There is no other way. If you trust the Lord Jesus He will forgive your sins and make your heart clean. Then you will be able to show others, too, how to get their hearts clean.

The Right Way to Walk

A certain chief noticed four young men strutting proudly about town. "Bring those young men to me," he ordered. "You four have been strutting about my town as though you own it," he scolded. To one of them he said: "Tell me, what makes you act like a rooster who thinks the sun rises only to hear him crow?"

"May your life be long, O Chief," replied the young man. "I walk like that because in all this town there is no one stronger than I."

The chief stood up. "In that case I challenge you to wrestle," he said. Then he picked the young man up, held him over his head, and threw him to the ground. "Don't let me see you strut around this town again," he commanded.

The chief turned to the second youth. "What is your reason for parading around this town as though you were the only donkey that could bray?" he asked.

"Long life to you, O Chief," the youth replied. "I walk like that because no one has finer clothes or more costly jewelry than I have."

The chief whispered a command, and immediately his servants brought in his beautiful clothes and jewelry. Everybody gasped at the sight of such riches.

"So, no one has finer clothes and jewelry than you?" he said to the young man. "Do you not know your chief? Don't you dare strut around my town like that anymore."

To the third young man the chief said: "Tell me, why do you walk about my town as though you were the only hyena that had spots?"

27

"May your life be long, O Chief," began the youth. "My pride is in my great knowledge. It excels that of every other person in this town."

Immediately the chief began to ask him questions about law, religion, medicine, and history. The youth failed to answer even one of the questions.

"Can a thorn bush boast of its fruit in the presence of an orange tree?" the chief asked. The shamefaced youth followed his two friends in disgrace.

The chief spoke to the fourth young man. "Those who boasted of superior strength, finery, and knowledge have left humbled and ashamed," he said sternly. "Now it is your turn to tell me why you walk the streets of my town with your head held so high."

The youth knelt before the chief. "May your life be long, O Chief," he said, respectfully. "I walk with my head high because, wherever I go, I walk with truth."

The chief was silent. Then he said: "You are right. Truth is something that every man should keep with him, always. There is no guilt or shame for the one who walks with truth."

He smiled at the young man, who was still kneeling. "Go," he told him. "You may continue to walk in my town with your head held high."

God is pleased with us when we speak the truth in our hearts. He wants us to love truth, speak truth, and act the truth in our daily lives. How can we do that? Jesus said: "Your word is truth" (John 17:17). We learn how to walk with truth by reading God's Word every day and doing what it tells us to do.

Why Chickens Lay Eggs

In the days when chickens could fly like birds, Vulture and Hen were friends. They lived together and did everything together. One day Hen pointed with her beak across the grasslands where they lived. "I wonder what is beyond all this?" she said. "I want to travel and see what is out there."

Vulture tried to persuade Hen to stay home, but she was determined to go. Vulture could not bear the thought of being separated from her friend, so they set out together.

At last their travels brought them to the place where Man lived. Vulture was afraid of such strange creatures. She wanted to leave. But Hen was excited. She wanted to see more.

When Man saw the birds he decided to try and catch them. He put out grain for them to eat.

"It's a trap," said Vulture. "Stay away from it." But Hen flew down and greedily began to peck the grain. Vulture stayed on a high branch and tried to persuade Hen to leave.

"Fly away with me," she begged. "Man has set a trap for us. He will surely eat us!"

But greedy Hen replied: "No, Vulture, I like this food. You may go if you wish, but I have decided to stay here."

The moment she made this choice, Hen lost her power to fly. She could only walk or run, or flutter short distances. Vulture continued to beg her to leave. "Man will feed you and keep you just so he can eat you! Run away from him!" But Hen refused to leave.

At last Vulture said: "Listen, Hen, and I will tell you how to prevent Man from killing you. Every day you must

29

Hen knew she was safe for another day.

lay him an egg. When Man sees the egg, he will say: 'My Hen has laid me an egg, so I will spare her today. Maybe another day I will kill her.'"

And that is why a chicken lays eggs...she doesn't want Man to eat her.

———————————

Hen was foolish to let herself get caught in Man's trap. We are foolish, too, if we let ourselves get caught in Satan's trap. And the more we keep on doing things that we know are wrong, the harder it is to get free from them. But there *is* a way to escape. In the Bible, a king named David said: "Surely He shall deliver you from the snare of the fowler" (Psalm 91:3). When you know that Satan is trying to trap you, ask the Lord for help. And remember, there are boys and girls all over the world who are being trapped by Satan, and who need someone to tell them that Jesus is the One who can help them escape.

Why Lizards Nod

One day a family of lizards went down to the river. There they saw a man climb into a boat and paddle to the other side. "If we could do that," said Papa Lizard, "we could cross the river too, and see what is on the other side."

"Then let's build a boat!" the son said.

"But what shall we build it with?" asked the daughter.

"Ask your father," said the wife.

Papa Lizard thought for a while. "The man's boat looks as though it is made of dried mud," he said. "Let's try that."

So they worked very hard and made a boat out of mud. Then they left it to bake in the sun. When they came back a few days later, the boat was hard and dry. "Looks good to me," Papa Lizard said. So they all got in and began to paddle to the other shore.

But the mud boat became softer and softer, until it melted away. Papa Lizard was strong enough to splash and kick his way to shore, where he climbed up on a rock and looked out over the water to see what had happened to his family. But they had all drowned.

And that is why, to this day, there is a certain lizard that sits in the sun and nods his head three times. He is saying: "Alas for my wife! Alas for my son! And alas for my daughter!"

Some people, like the Lizard family, put their trust in things that can never get them to where they want to

32

go...heaven. The only one who can take us there is Jesus. Without Him, nobody can make it. "I am the way, the truth, and the life," He said. "No one comes to the Father except through Me" (John 14:6).

The Frog and the Butter Pat

Two little frogs were playing in a small pool near a farmer's house. They saw the farmer's wife set a calabash, a large bowl, on a shaded rock beside the door, and go into the house.

The two frogs blinked their bulgy eyes. What was in that bowl? They turned their heads this way and that, looking and listening. Then they sprang as far as they could...hop, hop, hop...to the stone on which the calabash sat. Then, hop, hop, and a jump, right over the side and into a pool of smooth white stuff. It was milk!

They swam for a little while, but soon decided that their own pool was much more pleasant. But when they tried to jump out, they couldn't. The milk was too deep. They splashed and they kicked, but it was no use. They were two frightened little frogs.

At last one frog said: "I'm too tired to try anymore. My days are finished!" With that he closed his eyes and slowly sank to the bottom.

When the other frog saw that, he tried even harder to get out. After a while he realized that something strange was happening. His kicking and splashing was churning the milk into butter! Excited, he kept at it until there was a big pat of butter floating on top of the milk...and he was sitting on it!

Then it was easy to get out. He jumped right over the side of the calabash and landed on the rock. Then, hop, hop, hop and... "splash," the cool water of his own pool closed over his head.

The two little frogs struggled desperately to get out.

Frog never forgot the lesson he learned in that calabash. When his friends asked about his adventure, he would say, simply: "I didn't give up."

Do you sometimes feel that being a Christian is too hard? Do you feel like giving up? Don't! If you are really trying to be the kind of person the Bible tells you you should be, God will help you. A verse in the Bible says: "I can do all things through Christ who strengthens me" (Philippians 4:13).

Twenty Days

Once there was a selfish chief who had so much land he could not farm it all. But to make sure that no one else would farm it either, he passed a law that anyone who did so would be put to death. One day a poor stranger named Yon came along. Not knowing about the law, and seeing the unused land, he cut down a few trees and bushes and planted a little garden. When the chief heard about this he was furious.

"You have broken the law," he told Yon harshly. "You must die!"

"Long may you live, O Chief," Yon replied gently, "but I did not know about the law. The land was not being used, and I thought it better to grow a little food than to become a beggar, or even to starve."

"That's not the point!" the chief snarled. "You took my land like a thief! The law says you must die! After twenty days in prison you will be put to death!"

"If it must be so, it must be so," Yon replied quietly. "But I ask a favor. My parents are old and live very far from here. May I use the twenty days to go and say goodby to them?"

"Do you think I am a fool?" the chief bellowed. "If I let you go, you would never return!"

Yon looked steadily and calmly at the chief. "I give you my word," he said. "I will return."

Then a young man stepped forward. "May your life be long, O Chief," he said. "I am Yon's friend. If you will let him go, I will take his place in prison. And if he does not return you may take my life instead."

37

"What?" exclaimed the chief. "Do you really think he would come back?"

"Yes," Yon's friend replied. "He will keep his promise, whatever it may cost him."

"Very well," the chief agreed. "But remember, your life depends on him."

Turning to Yon, he said: "Go. You have twenty days."

It took Yon a whole week to reach his village. There he spent two sad days with his parents before setting out on the return trip.

But as he journeyed a terrible storm came up, and Yon lost his way. He found himself wandering over mountains and through swamps and jungles. For days he struggled on, hungry, tired, cold, and wet.

On the nineteenth day, the chief went to the prison. "See?" he sneered. "Your friend has not returned. And tomorrow is the last day!"

"He will keep his word," Yon's friend replied. "I trust him completely."

Next morning Yon's friend was taken before the chief. "The time is up," the chief said. "You must die."

"Long may you live, O Chief," the young man replied, "but the twentieth day is only begun. My friend has until evening to get here."

The chief laughed. "And you still think he will return?" he mocked. "Don't you know that he has left you to die in his place?"

But even as he spoke, Yon entered. Thin from hunger, his clothes tattered, his feet sore and bleeding, Yon took his place beside his friend.

The chief listened in amazement as Yon told his story. When he was finished, the chief said in a strangely quiet voice: "And you did all that so that you might die?"

"No, sir," Yon corrected him. "So that I might keep my word."

The chief shook his head in wonder. At last he spoke. "I cannot kill a man who is as honorable as you are," he said. "You are free to go. And I will change the law so that you may keep your garden."

38

Before Jesus went back to heaven, after He had died on the cross and been raised from the dead, He promised His friends that He would return. "I will come again," he said, "and receive you to Myself; that where I am, there you may be also" (John 14:3). We don't know when that will be, but we do know that He will keep His promise. And when He comes, those who love Him will go to live with Him. That's why Jesus also commanded His friends to tell people all over the world about Him. He wants them to be His friends so they can be with Him too.

The Snake in the Pot

Many years ago there lived a very wealthy chief, called Aga, whose most precious treasure was his small son, Oma. One evening Oma rushed home. "O Father," he said excitedly, "I have been listening to the beautiful songs of the praise singers at the shoemaker's house. I am going to give them a penny!"

Jealousy clutched Aga's heart. Why had the traveling praise singers gone to the shoemaker's house before they came to *his*? Wasn't *he* the chief? Shouldn't they come to *him* first?

Oma rushed into an inner room and out again, clutching a penny. Aga sank back on his mat. He remembered how the people of the town praised the shoemaker: "Though he is very poor," they would say, "he gives food to the hungry, water to the thirsty, and even shoes to the penniless. At night he keeps a fire burning in his entrance hut to welcome travelers to warmth and safety."

Aga jumped up. "I will see for myself," he said. He threw a dark blanket over his royal robe, and slipped out into the night. The drumming and chanting of the singers guided him to the poor shoemaker's hut, where he watched from behind a cornstalk fence.

Three drummers beat with bare hands on small wooden drums, and in front of them stood the chief singer in a long white robe. The crowd clapped and nodded at his words of praise for the shoemaker.

Aga saw the shoemaker motion for silence. "My heart is warmed with your praises," he said. "But you know I am

40

Aga slipped a deadly snake into the water pot.

a poor man and cannot pay you for your songs. I beg you to go where you will receive large gifts and money."

The chief singer bowed low before the shoemaker. "O kind sir," he said, "have we not heard of your many unselfish deeds? Today we do not sing for money, but for love."

Chief Aga crept back to his palace. Anger raged in his heart. Was *he* not the most important person in town? If only there was some way to get rid of the shoemaker. But how?

He thought long and hard. Then he had it! The shoemaker's water pot! That was the answer!

As sleep wrapped the town in darkness, Aga crept again along the path to the shoemaker's house. He slipped quietly inside and, yes, there was the water pot!

Carefully he took off the cover. Even more carefully he put a small but deadly snake into the pot. Then he replaced the cover and left.

Early in the morning a frightened man rushed into Aga's palace. "Long may you live, O Chief," he shouted. "Come quickly!"

Aga followed the man to the shoemaker's house. As they came near they heard loud wailing. The crowd moved aside to let the chief pass. The shoemaker was kneeling on the ground, tears running down his cheeks. Beside him lay Oma.

Aga gathered his son in his arms. "Oma! Oma, my son, my only son...speak to me!"

Oma opened his eyes. "Father," he whispered weakly, "the snake...it was in the pot...I wanted a drink...." His eyes closed and his breathing stopped.

Grief-stricken, Aga ran into the forest screaming: "My son, my son!" But it was too late to be sorry. Oma was dead. The people of the town found Aga a few days later, dead of a broken heart.

Aga did his terrible deed because he was jealous. The Bible says that jealousy is sin. It makes us do mean and hurtful things. The good news is that Jesus can help us control jealous feelings. If we will let Him live in our hearts, He will help us be kind and thoughtful instead. Aga's sinfulness made him very sad. Doing things to please God makes us happy. The Bible says it will "be well with us when we obey the voice of the Lord our God" (Jeremiah 42:6).

King Speed and King Dodging

Foxes and leopards don't normally travel together, but once there were two who always did. They liked being together because each had an unusual ability. They were always challenging each other to do impossible things. Because of his incredible speed Leopard had been named King Speed. And because Fox could dodge nimbly about he was called King Dodging.

One day as King Speed and King Dodging traveled together, they saw a storm coming. The sky grew black, and the wind roared through the trees as though warning them to hang on or they would be blown away.

"We'll get wet," King Speed said, as the storm reached them. "What's the plan?"

King Dodging replied: "Each to his own plan."

Just then the rain began to fall from the clouds. But before it could reach them, King Speed cut branches from the trees nearby, stuck them in the ground, peeled strips of bark to tie everything together, cut long grass to cover the poles, and took shelter in his grass hut just in time to keep from getting wet.

King Dodging watched him until the first drops began to patter down around him. Then he dodged this way and that way between the drops until the rain stopped. In this way he, too, avoided getting wet.

After the rain stopped, King Speed stepped out of his grass hut. But the ground was wet and he slipped in the mud at the doorway.

While he was still in the air, King Dodging challenged him: "All right," he said, "now let's see some speed!"

Before King Speed reached the ground, he snatched a knife from his belt, cut long slender palm leaves with it, wove a mat, spread it out, and landed on it.

Both kings said together: "Well done!" and continued on their way as though nothing unusual had happened.

Did you know that the Bible says: "With God all things are possible?" (Mark 10:27). Oh, we don't ask God to do funny things like our story talks about. But when we walk with God, it's adventure all the way, because God does unexpected and seemingly-impossible things. There is nothing He cannot do!

A Gift of Colors

One day a woman went into the forest to gather palm nuts. She climbed into a tree, but a branch gave way under her weight and she fell to the ground. Her leg was badly hurt, and she could not walk. It was a lonely place. She called for help again and again, but there was no one to hear. "What shall I do?" she wondered fearfully.

Then she heard the flutter of wings, and Pigeon landed nearby.

"Oh, kind Pigeon," called the woman, "please fly to my village and tell my people that I am hurt and unable to move."

"Humph!" exclaimed Pigeon. "I am much too busy to be bothered." And he flew away.

After a while Hawk came by in search of a mouse. He saw the woman lying on the ground and came close to her.

"Kind Hawk," said the woman, "take these palm nuts and eat them so you will have strength to fly to my village and tell my husband to come. My leg is broken, and I cannot move it."

Hawk just laughed and flew away. "I have no time to carry messages for foolish women," he called back as he went.

Then a plain brown bird landed beside the distressed woman. It was Kingfisher. "I see you are hurt," he said gently. "Would you like me to fly to your village and tell your people to come for you?"

"Oh yes, please do," replied the woman. Immediately Kingfisher soared into the sky. Before long the woman's

Kingfisher offered to help the injured woman.

relatives came for her.

Some time later, when the woman was almost well, Kingfisher came to see how she was.

"Oh, Kingfisher," exclaimed the grateful woman, "you are the kindest and best of birds! I shall give you beautiful colors to match your kind heart so that all may know that you are special."

She took the dyes she used for making beautiful cloth and painted the plain brown bird in bright colors of purple, green, and blue. And the delighted Kingfisher has proudly worn those colors ever since.

Kingfisher was beautiful inside. That's why the woman made him beautiful outside. She wanted it to show. If *we* are beautiful inside it will show on the outside, too. Jesus is the one who can make us truly beautiful inside. The Bible says: "If anyone is in Christ, he is a new creation" (2 Corinthians 5:17). It's having Jesus in our hearts that makes the difference. Aren't you glad you know that? Don't you wish everybody knew it?

The Heavenly Visitor

A long time ago, it is said, there was a village where four men lived. One was lame, one was bald, one was blind, and one was very, very poor. One day a visitor came to the village. The people didn't know it, but he was an angel in disguise. He asked each of the four men the same question: "What do you want more than anything else?"

The lame man said: "The use of my legs!"

The bald man said: "My hair!"

The blind man said: "My sight!"

And the very, very poor man said: "Enough money to buy food and clothes for my family."

"Very well," the heavenly visitor said, "you shall have what you want." Immediately the lame man could walk, the bald man had hair again, the blind man could see, and the poor man had a bag of money.

"Oh, thank you!" they exclaimed. "We will never ever forget your kindness!"

A long time passed and the angel returned to see if the four men were still grateful. First he went to the man who had been lame. The man recognized him and thought, selfishly: "I suppose he's come to ask for money or something, just because he did me a favor. Well, he's not getting anything!"

So he lied when the visitor asked him: "How are your legs now?"

"Not much better than they were before," he complained. "You didn't do a very good job on them, really."

The visitor was disappointed. "In that case," he said,

"there wasn't much point in making them better." And the man became lame again.

Next he went to the man who had been bald. That man, too, recognized the visitor and thought: "If he thinks I'm going to do him a favor just because he did one for me, he's wrong. I won't."

So when the visitor asked: "How do you like your hair?" he shrugged his shoulders and said: "Oh, it's all right, I suppose. But it has to be washed and cut and combed and all that. It's a bit of a nuisance, really."

"I see," said the angel, sadly. "Well, maybe you'd be better off without it." And the man became bald again.

The attitude of the man who had been blind was the same. "Now that I can see," he complained, "I have to do everything for myself. People don't help me like they used to."

"I understand," the angel said, and the man lost his sight once again.

Lastly, the angel went to the man who had been poor. He found him living in a nice house. He had nice clothes and lots of food. The angel knocked on the door and asked: "Please, could I have a drink of water? I'm very hot and thirsty."

This man didn't even recognize his visitor, but he answered: "Of course! Come in! And have supper with us too!"

After supper the angel asked: "Tell me, why are you so kind and generous to a stranger like me?"

"A long time ago I was very poor," the man replied. "Then one day a stranger came and helped me. Ever since then I have had a house to live in, and clothes to wear, and enough food for all my family. To show my thanks, I gladly share what I have with others."

"And because you do," the angel said, "your blessings will continue."

The Bible reminds us to show hospitality, "for by so doing some have unwittingly entertained angels" (Hebrews 13:2). When we think of all the good things we have, and of all the people in the world who have so little, we should be very thankful. And we should show our gratefulness by sharing what we have with others. If we are truly thankful to God for loving us and sending Jesus to die for us, we should show that too by telling others about Him. That's why Jesus said: "Go into all the world and preach the gospel to every creature" (Mark 16:15).

Vulture and Hawk

One day Vulture went out to hunt. He swooped down onto a rooftop and sat silently looking this way and that. Soon there was a swish of wings and Hawk landed beside him. They eyed each other for a few moments, and then Hawk asked: "What are you doing here?"

"What am I doing?" replied Vulture. "I am waiting for my supper to come to me."

"Aff!" exclaimed Hawk. "What a weakling you must be! I go hunting in my own strength." And he rose proudly into the sky.

Vulture watched him circle high above the trees and houses. Suddenly Hawk spied a nice fat rat. Vulture saw him go for it, dropping as straight and swiftly as an arrow. What Hawk didn't know, however, was that the rat was very close to a trap. With a great swish he swooped down. Too late...he was caught fast! The rat scurried away unharmed.

Vulture watched silently as Hawk struggled in vain to get out of the trap. Finally he lay still, exhausted.

Then Vulture spread his great wings and rose lazily from his perch. He circled once, then landed with a thud beside Hawk.

The frightened bird said: "Vulture, please go away!"

Vulture stood tall and straight. "No, indeed, I shall not," he said. "You are the one I was waiting for."

"But that's not fair!" Hawk said weakly.

"Is it not?" Vulture replied. "Were you not intending to make a meal of the rat?"

He came closer and fixed a beady eye on Hawk. "What

Vulture watched Hawk swoop down recklessly toward the trap.

good is your own strength now?" he asked.

———————————

Hawk found out too late that his own strength was not enough. Has that ever happened to you? Have you ever found yourself in trouble because you thought you could do something, then realized that you couldn't? If we are to please God and stay out of trouble we need a strength greater than our own.

There's a verse in the Bible that tells us where to find that strength. It says: "Wait on the Lord; be of good courage, and He shall strengthen your heart; wait, I say, on the Lord!" (Psalm 27:14). Jesus Christ will be your friend and helper, and give you all the strength you need for every situation.

The Royal Guest

There was once a very powerful king who loved to boast about his wealth. He and his family ate the very best food and wore the finest clothes. People came from long distances to see his beautiful home. One day the king paid a surprise visit to the home of a poor farmer. The frightened man bowed low before the king. "Long may you live, O King," he said nervously. He brought out his best mat for the king to sit on. How shabby it looked next to such rich clothing!

The farmer's youngest son, Auta, appeared in the doorway. "Come in son," said the farmer. "Our king has come to visit us."

Auta bowed very low before the king. "Long may you live," he said respectfully, seating himself at the king's feet.

Auta did not know that *he* was the reason for the king's visit. He was a very intelligent boy whose wise comments amazed everyone. Eventually his wisdom had become the talk of the whole kingdom. Now the king had come to hear the boy's words for himself.

The king ignored Auta at first, while he boasted about his wealth, his expensive clothing, his beautiful horses, and his home. "No other home in the land can compare with mine!" he finished grandly.

"No," Auta said firmly. "My home is better than yours."

The king was shocked and angry. "How dare you talk to me like that!" he shouted. "Look at this miserable house! Its walls are cracked and its roof is sagging. How dare you say it is better than my splendid palace?"

"Long may you live, O King," Auta replied steadily, "but my house is better than yours."

The vain king was furious. "Why do you say that?" he shouted. "Speak up, boy!"

"I say that, sir," the boy answered calmly, "because," and he smiled at the king, "because *you* are in my house!"

The surprised king stared at the lad. Then a smile began to creep across his face. "My boy," he said softly, "you are indeed wise. Today you have taught me a very important lesson."

———————————

Auta knew that what really mattered was not *what* was in his house, but *who* was in it. That is true of our hearts, too. The most important guest we can have in our hearts is the Lord Jesus Christ. He is not only the great King, He is the one who can save us from sin. He can make us truly happy, no matter what kind of a house we live in. In the Bible, Jesus said: "Behold, I stand at the door and knock. If anyone hears My voice and opens the door, I will come in" (Revelation 3:20).

Banana Town

One day Spider decided that the food in his town wasn't good enough. "I'm going to look for better food," he said greedily, and started on his journey.

After walking for many hours he came to a village.

"What place is this?" he asked some grasshoppers who happened by.

"Cassava Town," they replied proudly. "It is where we live. Come and eat with us. Cassava is the best food to be found anywhere."

Spider was hungry and said he would be happy to eat with them. Soon a bowl of steaming cassava was placed before him. But as he was about to take a mouthful, he noticed some smoke rising in the distance.

"Is that another town?" he asked.

"Yes. That is where mice live," the grasshoppers replied. "They call it Bean Town."

Now Spider liked beans better than cassava, so he rudely jumped up and hurried toward the smoke, his mouth watering all the way.

"Is this the way to Bean Town?" he asked some mice who were returning from market.

"Yes," they answered. "And you will not find fatter beans no matter how far you travel. Come and share our dinner with us."

"Oh, thank you!" said Spider. "I'm terribly tired and hungry." He followed them to their town, where the mice happily cooked beans for him. But again, just as he was about to eat, Spider saw smoke rising from another village.

Ungrateful Spider thought the food in the next village would be better.

"What place is that?" he asked.

"That is where the monkeys live," answered the mice. "They call it Rice City. It is such a long way away you would have to eat a lot of beans to give you the strength to get there."

But greedy Spider liked rice even better than he liked beans. He wanted to save all the room in his stomach for rice. So without even saying thank you, he left his meal and started off. But Rice City was indeed a long way off, and before Spider got there he was so weak from hunger he could hardly walk straight. Only the thought of steaming bowls of rice kept him going.

At last he got there and was welcomed by the monkeys, who began cooking him a feast of rice. Oh, it smelled good! At last Spider lifted the first spoonful to his mouth, but as he did he saw smoke rising from yet another village. He couldn't resist asking: "What is that place?"

"We don't know," answered the monkeys. "It is so far away we have never been there. Some people say it is Banana Town, but nobody knows for sure."

"Banana Town?" thought Spider. Could it be true? Of all the food in the world, Spider liked bananas best. Could there actually be such a place as Banana Town? Ungrateful Spider, even though he was weak from hunger, staggered to his feet and stumbled on his way.

At long last, too exhausted to walk, Spider dragged himself into the unknown village, and fainted. When he woke up, he looked...and rubbed his eyes in disbelief. Poor, greedy, hungry Spider was back in his own home town.

Some people, like Spider, don't appreciate the good things they have or the kind things that other people do for them. The Bible tells us: "In everything give thanks; for this is the will of God in Christ Jesus for you" (1 Thessalonians 5:18). We should not only be thankful to other people, we should be thankful to God too. He loves us so much that He sent Jesus to be our Savior. One way to show that we are thankful is to tell other people about Jesus, and to pray for missionaries who take that good news to people in other countries.

The King's Ring

In a certain town, two boys were always together...at school, at play, at market, everywhere. Many people thought they were twins, or at least brothers. But they were neither twins nor brothers. Bawa was the son of poor parents who were servants in the king's palace. Nuhu was the favorite son of the king himself. Could there be a greater difference?

Because Bawa's parents were trusted and faithful, the two boys were allowed to play together every day. As they grew older they spent more and more time together.

After a while, the kindhearted king arranged for Bawa to move into his palace, where he lived just like Nuhu's brother. By the time the boys had grown up, everyone seemed to have forgotten that Bawa was only a servant boy.

At last the time came for Bawa to leave the palace. His parents had arranged for him to marry a beautiful young woman and start his own home.

As the two young men were having their last meal together, Bawa said: "Nuhu, I'd like you to give me something of yours to remind me of you always."

"That's a good idea," replied Nuhu. "What would you like?"

Bawa had always admired the silver ring that Nuhu wore. "I would like to have your ring," he said. "It would make me think of you every time I looked at it on my hand."

Nuhu wanted to please his friend, but he knew that he could not part with his beautiful ring. It was really the king's ring...the seal of the kingdom that Nuhu would someday inherit from his father.

"I'd like to give you my ring, Bawa," he said slowly, "but there is a better way for you to remember me."

Bawa was excited. "What could be better?" he asked eagerly.

"To *not* grant your request," Nuhu said gently. "You will remember me even better when you look at your hand and see that I did *not* give you the ring."

Do we sometimes ask our friends or parents...or even God...for the wrong things? God wants to answer our prayers, but He may have to say "no" if we ask for selfish reasons. We can always trust Him, though, to answer our prayers in the best way because He loves us. In fact, the Bible tells us that God delights in giving us what we ask from Him when "we keep His commandments and do those things that are pleasing in His sight" (1 John 3:22).

The Wealthy Mouse

A country mouse became very tired of being poor. He decided to leave home and seek his fortune. His neighbors ridiculed him. "Aha," they said, "you are not satisfied with living in our field with us poor mice. You want to be better than we are. Well, be gone, and may you get what you deserve."

So he left.

For a long time no one heard from him. Some of his friends even forgot about him.

Then one day he returned. He was very wealthy. He had a bag of gold, splendid clothes, and a brightly colored umbrella. He was sleek and fat. Immediately he was a hero. Everyone wanted to be his friend, even those who had laughed at him.

One day he was approached by some mice, who said: "We want to go where you went, and find wealth like you did. Is there enough for us too?"

"Ah yes," replied the wealthy mouse, "but I don't think you really want to go."

"Oh yes we do," they insisted. "Will you tell us how to get there?"

"All right," said the wealthy mouse. "The way will take you right across the cat's nose. Do you still want to go?"

There was silence. His friends didn't answer him. And not one of them left to seek his fortune.

It's easy to want something very much...unless it's hard

Wealthy Mouse pointed the way to riches.

to get. Jesus said: "Lay up for yourselves treasures in heaven" (Matthew 6:20). That's the best kind of wealth there is. One way of getting it is to tell others about Jesus. As they trust Him as Savior, you have treasures in heaven. But sometimes doing that is difficult. Like the cat in our story, Satan will try to stop us. Or people may ridicule us.

Don't let that stop you from trying. It will be wonderful when you get to heaven and find treasure waiting for you!

Jackal and Heron

It was evening. Jackal emerged from his hideout. The chirp of bush fowl made him prick up his ears. "Just what I need for my supper," he thought. He crept to a clearing where five bush hens were scurrying around searching for food. They were almost full-grown, but still young and tender.

Jackal crouched in the tall grass, moving nothing but his eyes. "Will they never come close enough?" he complained.

As though in answer to his question, one hen began to chase an insect straight toward him. Jackal tensed...and sprang. The unsuspecting bird didn't have a chance.

Jackal was pleased with himself. His supper had come to him quickly. "Too bad I can only catch one at a time," he thought. As he swallowed his last mouthful he cried in sudden pain. A sharp bone had stuck in his throat.

"Ooowww! Oh my goodness, what shall I do?" he wailed. He shook his head, jumped up and down, and rolled on the ground...but nothing moved the bone. Choking and coughing, he called: "Who will help me? Ooowww...won't somebody please help me?"

"What are you moaning about, Jackal?" Jackal stopped his rolling and looked into the eyes of Rabbit.

"Please, Rabbit, pull the bone out of my throat," begged Jackal.

Rabbit kept his distance. "I know you too well to believe that bone-in-the-throat story," he scolded. "You want me for your supper too!" And Rabbit hopped away.

Other animals came along but each one had a reason for

"If you move I'll stab you with my beak!" Heron warned Jackal.

not helping Jackal.

He made his way to a pool to see if a drink would help. There he met Heron having her final drink for the day. Heron saw him too, and immediately spread her wings.

"Stop! Don't leave!" cried the desperate Jackal. "I'll give you a reward if you'll only help me. Please, please help me!"

Heron didn't move. There was no doubt that Jackal was in real trouble, but she was afraid.

Jackal fell on the ground and began clawing at his throat. "Yes, I will help him," Heron decided and moved slowly toward him.

"Sit up and open your mouth wide," she commanded. Jackal obeyed. "If you move I'll stab you with my beak!" she warned fiercely. Jackal sat as still as a stone, hardly daring to breathe.

Heron leaned forward until her head was almost in Jackal's wide open mouth. It took just a second for her to grasp the bone with her long beak and remove it.

"Thank you, Heron," said the relieved Jackal. "I will never forget your kindness." Then he turned to go home.

"Wait," said Heron. "Where is my reward?"

Jackal looked at her, his wide mouth turning up at the corners as though he were smiling. "Your reward is this," he replied. "You put your head in Jackal's mouth and it came out safely!"

Jackal wasn't really grateful, even though Heron helped him so much. Sometimes we behave like that, too...especially with God. He helps us in so many ways, but we don't always thank Him the way we should. First of all, of course, we should thank Him for sending His Son, Jesus, to die for us. God wants us also to show that we are thankful by sharing His love with others, and by being "kind to one another, tenderhearted, forgiving one another" (Ephesians 4:32).

Old Shorty Legs

Long ago all the animals lived on an island in a river. They chose Turtle to be their king because he was so strong and beautiful. His shell was all one piece, smooth and shiny as a pearl. The animals often wondered what it was like on the other side of the river, but there was no way to get across. King Turtle liked it that way because he didn't want to lose any of his subjects...or their admiration.

Every morning he would say: "Is not my shell the most beautiful thing in the world?" And the animals would answer: "True, O King. It is indeed the most splendid thing we have ever seen!"

There was just one thing that bothered Turtle...he didn't like being so short.

One morning as he went for a stroll he heard voices in the bushes. "A tree has fallen across the river!" someone said excitedly. "Now we can get across!"

A bridge! Turtle felt sick. Now there was no way he could keep the animals on the island.

Then he heard another voice. "Shh!" it said. "Don't let old Shorty Legs hear about it. He might not let us go."

Old Shorty Legs? Turtle became so angry he could hardly make his stubby little legs move. "I'll show them," he raged. "I may be short, but I am strong...stronger than any of them...yes, stronger than all of them put together."

So he called all the animals together.

"I have a surprise for you," he began. "I arranged for a tree to fall across the river last night so that there would be a bridge. Not only that, but I have planned to take you all

68

across and show you the wonderful things on the other side. And not only that," he continued proudly, "I have decided we shall have a parade...and all of you shall ride on my beautiful back!"

There was a great "Ooohhh!" from the crowd. "But, O King," someone said, "surely you are not strong enough to carry all of us?"

"Yes I am!" roared Turtle. "Now climb on, all of you!"

But King Turtle was not as strong as he thought he was. When the last animal, Elephant, climbed on, there was a great cra-a-ck and Turtle's beautiful shell split into pieces!

Everyone felt sorry for poor Turtle. So they patched him up as best they could with leaves and bark and mud, but his shell was never smooth and shiny again. And because he was the first turtle, all his children since then have patched-up looking shells.

Turtle was lucky. He could have gotten himself completely squashed...all because he was so proud and boastful. The Bible tells us: "Pride goes before destruction, and a haughty spirit before a fall" (Proverbs 16:18). It also tells us that "God resists the proud, but gives grace to the humble" (James, 4:6). Remember that the next time you see a turtle!

The Prickly Visitor

What a day it was! Rainy, cold, wet...the kind of weather that made Squirrel stay in his hole where it was warm. Hedgehog, however, had been wandering about until she was cold all over. Just then she came to Squirrel's hole. "I'm very cold," she told her. "Do you have room in there for me too?"

"Not really," Squirrel replied. "It's quite small. But you are welcome to share its warmth with me."

Hedgehog, who was more than twice as big as Squirrel, struggled in and immediately curled up into a round, wet ball. Poor Squirrel had to squirm and twist and wriggle to keep away from Hedgehog's stiff, thorny hairs.

Finally the uncomfortable little animal said: "Really, Hedgehog, it's not pleasant living with you. You're full of prickles. You must go and settle in a place of your own."

But Hedgehog didn't budge. "What do you mean, move?" she said. "I like it here. If you're unhappy, you're the one who should move."

Squirrel tried to be friends with Hedgehog, but it didn't work because Hedgehog didn't care about Squirrel. It's sad when that kind of thing happens to people. We all need friends...the right kind. We read in the Bible that "A man who has friends must himself be friendly" (Proverbs 18:24). Jesus is the best friend anyone can have because He cares so much for us. And when He is our friend, we want other people to know about Him so they can be His friends, too.

Squirrel tried his hardest to get away from Hedgehog's prickles.

The Poor Man and the Beggar

A certain man was very poor...so poor that he had to sell all his goods, one by one, just to buy food. At last he had nothing left except the tattered clothes on his back. He became so unhappy that he wanted to die. He made his way to the palace and asked to see the king. He was brought into the throne room and bowed low before the great man. The king wondered what had brought this man into the palace dressed in such rags.

"What business has brought you?" he asked.

Without even raising his head, the poor man said: "Long may you live, O King. I have come because I am tired of the struggle to live. I had no food yesterday, and I have none for today or for tomorrow. Please command your soldiers to kill me."

"You are very foolish to ask such a thing," the king replied. "But if that is what you want, so be it."

He called two of his soldiers. "Take this man and put him out of his misery," he ordered.

The soldiers led the poor man outside, where a crowd was gathering, as preparations were made to end his life. As the poor man waited, head down, he heard a voice say: "When he is dead, please may I have his clothes?"

The poor man looked up and saw a beggar who not only wore rags more tattered than his own, but who was also blind.

"Stop!" he said to the soldiers. "Take me back to the

king!"

The king was surprised to see the man still alive. "What now?" he asked.

"I beg you to let me live," the poor man said, falling full length before the king, "for today I have seen someone who is worse off than I am."

———————

Which is worse...being very poor, or very unhappy? God doesn't want us to be either. That's why the Bible teaches us that we should comfort the sad and help the poor. That's why it also teaches us that the way to be truly happy is to let Jesus control our lives. As our Savior, He not only makes us happy while we are on earth, He takes us to be with Him in heaven when we die. And that's why a man named Paul said: "Rejoice in the Lord always. Again I will say, rejoice!" (Philippians 4:4).

The Foolish Bird

One day Bird was quarreling with his dreaded enemy, Snake. Snake became very angry and threatened to eat Bird. Just as he was ready to strike, the wind brought a cloud of black smoke around them.

"Bush fire!" they both exclaimed in terror. Nothing was more feared than fire.

Bird immediately raised his wings to fly away. But Snake cried: "O friend Bird, please don't leave me behind. I cannot find a hole to hide in. Please carry me to safety!"

Bird let Snake wrap himself around his neck. Then he tried to fly. Snake was a heavy load, but at last Bird got off the ground. He managed to fly to a safe place where the fire had already been, and landed on a rock. But Snake remained wrapped around his neck.

"You can let go of me now," Bird reminded him.

"Oh no," replied the ungrateful Snake. "What else is there for me to eat in this burned-over place?"

And he ate the foolish Bird.

Bird listened to the wrong person...his enemy. Don't let that happen to you. It is foolish to listen to people who tell you to do things that may get you in trouble. A Christian should listen to what God says in the Bible. You can always count on that! "The entirety of Your word is truth," we read in Psalm 119:160.

74

Snake was so heavy, Bird could hardly fly.

Lost Treasure

Once there were three hunters who went hunting together, thinking they would catch bigger game that way. One day they hunted all morning but caught nothing. "Today we have no luck," the first hunter said. "Let's go home."

Just as he said this, the second hunter saw something in the bushes. Cautiously they moved toward it, only to find two large earthenware pots. "This is strange," the third hunter said. "What are pots doing in the forest?"

Carefully they removed the rags that had been stuffed into the necks of the pots, and tipped them over to see what was in them. Out came money!

"We're rich! We're rich!" they exclaimed together.

For a long time they talked about their new wealth, but they couldn't agree on how to divide it. At last the first hunter said: "I'm getting hungry. Let's go to the village so we can buy some food."

"But what shall we do with the money?" the second hunter said. "If we take it with us somebody might kill us to get it. And if we leave it here somebody else might find it."

"I know," said the third hunter. "You two go, and I'll stay here and guard the money."

"No," said the other two. "If we leave you might run away with it."

Finally they decided that the first hunter should go, and that the other two would keep an eye on the money...and each other.

After the first hunter had gone, the second hunter said:

"Treasure!" the hunters exclaimed. "We're rich!"

"You know, if there were only two of us we could have a whole pot of money each."

The more they thought about it, the greedier they became. By the time the first hunter returned with the food, they wanted the money so much that they killed him. Then they sat down to eat.

"I wonder why there is only enough food for two?" one hunter said, unwrapping the bundle.

"He must have eaten his meal in the village," the other said.

"Well," was the reply, "I hope he enjoyed it. He was such an innocent fellow."

But as they ate, they began to feel ill. Too late, they realized what had happened. "He has poisoned the food!" they cried. "What a wicked thing to do!"

And so it was that none of the three enjoyed the treasure. Their greed had killed them all.

Greed is a sin that can make us do very bad things. It reminds us that there is wickedess in everybody's heart...wickedness that can keep us from enjoying the greatest treasure of all...a place in heaven. The Bible tells us that if we are truly sorry for our sins God will forgive us. "If we confess our sins, He is faithful and just to forgive us our sins and to cleanse us from all unrighteousness" (1 John 1:9). If we do that, God will not only give us clean hearts, He will help us tell others how they, too, can be forgiven.

Why Spider Has a Tiny Waist

One day Elephant and Hippopotamus met on a jungle path. They were surprised to learn that both were celebrating special feast days, and both were looking for Spider. They wanted him to entertain their friends. "He's the greediest creature in the whole jungle," Elephant said. "I've never seen anyone with such a big stomach!"

"True," replied Hippo. "But he tells good stories."

"Only as long as we keep that stomach of his full!" laughed Elephant as they parted.

Before long Hippo found Spider sunning himself in a tree. "Ho, Spider!" he greeted. "I bring an invitation to our Hippo feast."

Spider's mouth began to water. "I'll be glad to attend," he said. "When will it be ready?"

"I'm not quite sure," said Hippo. "But I have a plan. If you tie this rope around your waist, I'll give the other end a tug when it's time to come."

Hippo handed Spider one end of the rope and disappeared down the path. Just then Elephant arrived. "Ho, Spider!" he called. "I've been looking for you. I've come to invite you to the Elephant feast. Will you come and tell us some of your stories?"

"Why, of course!" said Spider, eagerly. "I'd love to. Is it ready?"

"Not yet," replied Elephant. "I'll call you."

Now Spider had a problem. Hippo feasts were always good. But Elephant feasts were excellent too. He didn't want to miss either one.

79

Poor Spider was pulled both ways at once.

"I'll tell you what to do," said Spider. "Bring me a rope. I'll tie one end around my waist, and when your feast is ready give it a tug and I'll come."

Elephant brought a rope and gave one end to Spider. Then he went off to his village holding the other end. Greedy Spider then tied *both* ropes around his waist and went back to dozing in the sun, thinking of two feasts.

After a while he felt a tug on Hippo's rope. Immediately he jumped up and started down the path toward Hippo Village. But as he ran, he was jerked back suddenly by a tug on Elephant's rope. "Hey!" shouted Spider, "not both at once!"

But Hippo and Elephant couldn't hear him. They kept on pulling...first one, then the other. At last they both went to see why Spider hadn't come. They found him in a heap, covered with dirt, and squeezed nearly in two.

"Silly Spider," they said, looking at his tiny, tiny waist. "Don't you know you can't go two ways at once?"

Spider's greed prevented him from seeing how foolish he was being. Jesus told us: "No one can serve two masters" (Matthew 6:24). God wants you to follow Him, but Satan tries to pull you his way instead. You have to decide which one you will follow. Whenever you see a spider, remember...you can't go two ways at once.

Why Dogs Chase Trucks

A truck driver became tired of trying to avoid the animals that always wandered across the roads. So he called a meeting of all the animals and told them that if they wanted to cross the road they must pay two dollars. One day Goat wandered onto the road. Truck Driver stopped him and asked for his money. But Goat refused to pay. Instead, he dashed across the road and disappeared into the bushes. Since then, Goat always runs fast across the road so Driver can't catch him.

The next day Sheep started across the road. When Truck Driver stopped him, he meekly paid his money. Because Sheep paid, he isn't afraid anymore. He just saunters across, or even stops halfway.

Next, Truck Driver stopped Dog. Dog didn't have the right money, so he gave him five dollars and asked for change. Truck Driver went to his truck pretending to get it, but instead he drove off. And that is why Dog continues to bark and chase after cars...he wants his change.

And that is why some animals act as they do...or so we are told.

Do you know why you do what you do?

When we do wrong things it is because of sin in our hearts. The Bible says: "The wages of sin is death, but the gift of God is eternal life in Christ Jesus our Lord" (Romans 6:23). When we receive this wonderful gift from God, then we will want to do right things to please Him.

Truckdriver made a deal with the animals.

The Thief and the Stick

Once there was a very wealthy man who had many servants. One morning he couldn't find a certain ring. It was a very special ring, and very expensive. He searched and searched, but it wasn't there. 'Is one of my servants a thief?" he wondered.

So he called them all together. Then he gave each one a stick of exactly the same length. "I am going out on business," he told them. "I will be back this evening. At that time I will know who the thief is, because his stick will be an inch longer than the others."

The servants looked at each other. "How can a stick grow?" they asked.

"You will see," the master said, and left.

Each servant put his stick in a safe place and went about his day's work. All the servants but one, that is. The real thief went to a place where he could be alone. Fearfully, he looked at his stick, first at one end, then at the other. "How can it be?" he wondered.

At last he had an idea. He took his stick and cut it off exactly one inch from the end. "Now it can grow and nobody will know," he said to himself, and went back to work.

When the master returned he called all the servants together. He took their sticks from them one at a time and measured each one carefully. None of them, however, had grown...but one stick was an inch shorter than the others.

Each of us has sinned against God. It is foolish to try

84

and hide those sins from Him. The Bible says: "Be sure your sin will find you out" (Numbers 32:23). It is better to admit our sins, and ask God to forgive them. He will, if we are sorry for our sins, because Jesus took the punishment for them when He died on the cross. We should be glad about that...and be sharing the good news with others.

Spider's Moon

Spider and his wife had a large rice farm. The rice grew well. The stalks were tall, the heads were full and heavy. It wasn't quite ripe enough, but Spider didn't want to wait any longer. The rice looked *so* good! He could almost taste it!

Finally Spider said to his wife: "Let's eat some of our new rice. It looks *so* good!"

"No," answered his wife. "It's not ripe yet. We can't eat it until the moon is full and round."

But Spider wanted that rice very badly. What could he do? Suddenly he remembered what his wife had said about the full moon.

He hurried to his garden and dug up a huge cassava root, which looked like a very long potato. He peeled it and cut off a nice round slice that looked just like a moon. That evening he climbed a tree and tied it to a branch.

He hurried to find his wife. "Wife!" he called. "Come and see the moon! Now we can eat our rice!"

His wife and all the neighbors ran outside to see Spider's moon. It looked very real, and Spider was certain that no one knew what he had done. Sure enough, his wife told him that they would eat new rice the very next day.

Just then a little boy spoke up. "That's not a real moon," he said. "It's just a piece of cassava."

"What do you know about moons?" said Spider angrily. "Go to bed!"

Instead of going to bed, the little boy got his bow and arrow and shot at Spider's moon. Everybody laughed as it fell from the tree and broke into pieces.

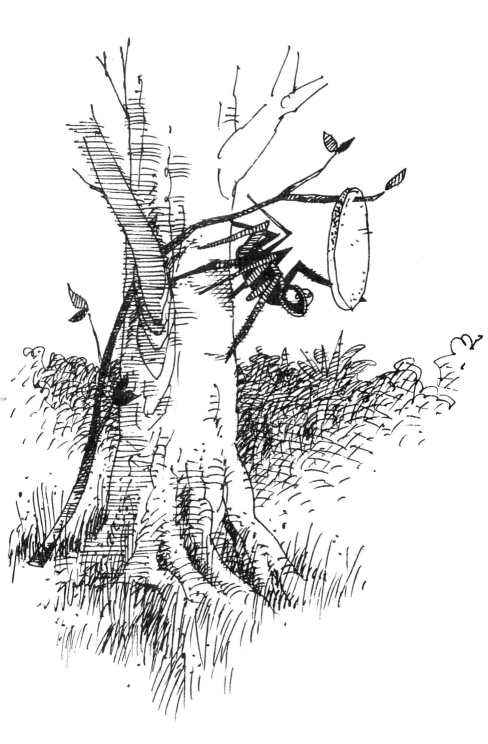

Foolish Spider was sure they would think it was the moon.

Foolish Spider disappeared into his house and did not eat new rice until the *real* full moon appeared.

Spider might have fooled a lot of people if the little boy hadn't seen through his trick. Satan, too, tries to fool people. He tells them that it's quite all right to do sinful things. The way to see through his tricks is to know the truth. That's why this verse is in the Bible: "Your word I have hidden in my heart, that I might not sin against You" (Psalm 119:11).

Monkey and Crocodile

In a muddy brown river that flowed through the jungle lived Crocodile. On the bank of the river was a large tree whose branches hung over the water. At the top of the tree lived Monkey. Every day Crocodile thought of ways that he could get close to Monkey...close enough to make a meal of him.

One day he called to Monkey: "Friend, I have a splendid idea! Come down and hear about it!"

Monkey dropped to a lower branch, but stayed well out of reach. "What is it?" he asked.

"I have heard that our friend Elephant who lives across the river is sick," said Crocodile. "Don't you think we should go and visit him?"

"That's impossible," answered Monkey. "I can't swim."

"No, but I can," replied Crocodile. "I'm an excellent swimmer. I can take you over on my back."

Monkey thought about it for a moment, and agreed to go. Crocodile moved closer to the tree, and Monkey dropped lightly onto his back.

Crocodile swam swiftly and smoothly toward the opposite shore. But halfway across he stopped and looked back at Monkey. "Oh, by the way," he said, "there's something you should know. The only medicine that will help Elephant get better is the heart of a monkey."

Monkey's quick mind sprang into action. He hopped on top of Crocodile's head where he was safe from his teeth, and said: "And there's something you should know too. Monkeys aren't like crocodiles. They don't always carry their hearts around with them. In fact, I left in such a hurry that I forgot

89

"Let's go back," Monkey told Crocodile. "I forgot my heart."

mine. It's still at home."

"Oh, that's no problem," said Crocodile. "We'll go back and get it." So he turned around and swam back to the tree. As he glided under its branches, Monkey swung nimbly out of sight.

"Hurry back!" Crocodile called. "We don't want to keep Elephant waiting!"

"Maybe you don't," Monkey shouted down from the treetop. "But I've changed my mind. When you see him, tell him he'll have to get better without my help!"

Monkey was safe when he stayed in his tree. He got into trouble when he forgot that, and went with Crocodile. Christians can get into trouble, too, when they forget what the Bible teaches, and do some of the things that people who don't love God do. There are many helpful prayers in the Bible. One of them is: "Direct my steps by Your word" (Psalm 119:133).

The Choice

Two friends named Hubba and Bubba wanted to marry the same girl. She did not know which one to choose, so she said: "I will marry the one who shows himself the braver." One evening they both went to visit her. When it came time to leave, she walked with them a little way along the path. Suddenly a leopard sprang out of the bushes.

Hubba threw his spear at it, but missed. Bubba threw his spear. He, too, missed.

"Hurry!" Hubba cried. "Bring more spears!"

Bubba dashed off while Hubba tried to distract the leopard from attacking the girl. For a little while the animal just swished its tail back and forth, but then it crouched, ready to spring.

Swiftly, Hubba took out his knife and jumped on the leopard, wrestling with it until he killed it. Then he sat the dead animal up on its haunches. "Lie down in front of it," he told the girl as he hid behind a bush.

Bubba reappeared, but without spears. He couldn't find any. When he saw the girl lying in front of the leopard he thought angrily: "Hubba is a coward! He has run away and left the leopard to kill her!"

In a frenzy of rage he sprang upon the leopard barehanded. He flung both arms around its neck in a terrible grip...only to fall over with a thud, the dead animal on top of him.

Then Hubba jumped out from behind the bush, and the girl got to her feet. In spite of the fright they all had had, they laughed and laughed together.

"Both of you have been very brave," the girl said. "Now I will make my choice."

Which one do you think she chose?

We all have decisions to make. The most important is whether we will let Jesus be our Savior and our master. There is a verse in the Bible which says: "Choose for yourselves this day whom you will serve" (Joshua 24:15). If you choose Jesus, He not only gives you eternal life, but He helps you in the other decisions you make day by day. And He will help you share this good news with others who don't know Him.